Schott New York

Hannah Lash
b.1981

November

for three sopranos with hand percussion

Score

ED 31260

www.schott-music.com

SCHOTT

Mainz · London · Madrid · New York · Paris · Prague · Tokyo · Toronto

November

Hannah Lash

11
Sop.
Bowl
Chime
mf
mp mf p mp
E - ven e - - ven e -

16
Sop.
Bowl
Chime
mf p f p f
ven the oak gives up its leaves
ven the oak gives up its leaves
ven the oak gives up its leaves

21
Sop.
Bowl
Sop.
Chime
Sop.
Chime
mf mp mf p mp mf p
E - ven e - - ven e - ven the
E - ven e - - ven e - ven
E - ven e - - ven e - ven
26
f p f fp f
oak gives up its leaves now
the oak gives up its leaves now
the oak gives up its leaves now

31
Sop.
mp mf mp f mp mf p fp
e - ven the oak gives up its leaves now
Bowl
Sop.
mp mf mp f mp mf p fp
e - ven the oak gives up its leaves now
Chime
Sop.
mp mf mp f mp mf fp
e - ven the oak gives up its leaves now
Chime

36
Sop.
f mp mf p mp mf
strewn care-less - ly strewn care-less -
Bowl
Sop.
f mp mf p mp mf
strewn care-less - ly strewn care-less -
Chime
Sop.
f mp mf p mp mf
strewn care-less - ly strewn care-less -
Chime

41
Sop.
Bowl
Chime
p mf f p
-ly strewn care - less - ly
46
mf mp mf p mp mf p
E - ven e - - ven e - ven the
E - ven e - - ven e - ven

51
Sop.
oak gives up its leaves now
like cast off
Bowl
Sop.
the oak gives up its leaves now
like cast off
Chime
Sop.
the oak gives up its leaves now
like
Chime
56
Sop.
clo-thing like cast off clo - thing stripped in pas-sion or need to find
Bowl
Sop.
clo - thing like cast off clo – thing stripped in pas - sion or need to find
Chime
Sop.
cast off clo-thing like cast off clo-thing stripped in pas-sion or
Chime

61
Sop.
bare ex - po-sure
Bowl
Sop.
bare ex - po - sure
Chime
Sop.
need to find bare ex - po - sure
Chime
66
Sop.
an es-sence an es-sence an es-sence an
Bowl
Sop.
an es-sence an es-sence an es-sence
Chime
Sop.
an es-sence an es-sence
Chime

71
Sop.
mf p
es - sence
p mf p
where bone
meets win -
Bowl
Sop.
p mf p
an es -- sence
p mf p<
where bone
meets
Chime
Sop.
p p mf p
an es-sence
an es - sence
p
where bone
Chime
76
Sop.
f p p mf p
- ter's harsh
touch
where bone
meets win -
Bowl
Sop.
f p p mf p<
win - ter's harsh touch
where bone
meets
Chime
Sop.
mf p f p p
meets win - ter's harsh touch
where bone
Chime

81
Sop.
- ter's harsh touch
Bowl
Sop.
win - ter's harsh touch
Chime
Sop.
meets win - ter's harsh touch
Chime

86
Sop.
Bowl
Sop.
Chime
Sop.
Chime

91
Sop.
Bowl
Sop.
Chime
Sop.
Chime
pp < p
p > pp
creep - ing
creep ing
96
creep - ing
in - to cren - e - la - tions
in - to cren - e - la - tions
in - to cren - e - la -
in - to cren - e - la-tions
in - to
pp p mp mf

101
Sop.
mp pp
cren - e - la - tions
pp
carved from years of
Bowl
Sop.
p mp pp
tions cren - e - la - tions
pp
carved from years of
Chime
Sop.
mp pp
cren - e - la - tions
pp
carved from years of
Chime
106
Sop.
mp p mp pp
strug - gle mere - ly to con - tin - ue
Bowl
Sop.
mp p mp pp
strug - gle mere - ly to con - tin - ue
Chime
Sop.
pp mp mp pp pp p
strug - gle Ev - en e - - ven e - ven
Chime

111
Sop.
Bowl
Sop.
Chime
mp
mp
ppp
Sop.
the oak gives up its leaves now
Chime